PLAYS AROUND THE WORLD

Folk Tales Adapted for the Stage

by
Lenore Blumenfeld

Xerox Education Publications

XEROX

CONTENTS

PROGRAM NOTES

These plays are drawn from tales that have delighted children around the world for countless generations.

Dialogue and basic stage directions are provided—but you'll find plenty of leeway for improvisation and self-expression.

As you read through the scripts you'll find opportunities for dance and song, pantomime, simple staging and lighting effects, cartwheel-turning and pudding-tossing.

You can use these plays for pure entertainment—or link them to classroom discussion of present–day topics. For example:

BRICRIU'S FEAST—a fragment of one of the oldest stories in the Ulster legend cycle—reflects the humor and pugnacity that characterize Irish literature. Also, the heralds' proclamations suggest the rhythm and phrasing of the Gaelic language.

THE SEAGULL TRAP—a *suk-tu* (legend-story) from the seventeenth–century pre-Russian culture of Alaska—shows that Eskimos have practiced wildlife conservation for centuries. In the play the seagulls teach the girl that being trapped and caged is a cruel fate for any living creature. The play also shows the Eskimos' great respect for needlework. In their harsh climate anyone who can make clothes warm and weatherproof is held in high regard.

TILL EULENSPIEGEL'S MERRY PRANKS—based on the life of an obscure peasant of fourteenth-century Germany—shows the evolution from fact to folklore to art. Although little is known about Till's activities, generations of storytellers have embroidered the blank spots of history with a collection of colorful episodes. Their tales, in turn, inspired Richard Strauss to compose a delightful tonepoem which uses music, not words, to describe Till's adventures.

THE KING MEETS HIS MATCH—a tale from India, often called "the birthplace of folklore"—uses snarling lions and playful jackals to show how wit can overcome brawn and bluster. The play also suggests the inevitable transfer of power and authority from parent to child.

TIGER'S WEDDING DAY—an African story carried by slave ship to the West Indies—shows that the prankster-hero is a distinctive character, appearing in the folklore of nations that are widely separated by both geography and culture. In the West Indies the traditional mischief-maker is Anansi, the Spider; in Germany he appears as Till Eulenspiegel; in our country he is Brer Rabbit—and interested students can easily unmask a practical joker in the folklore of many other lands.

ALENKA AND ALIONA—one of the *skazki* (peasant tales) of prerevolutionary Russia—shows the affection and loyalty between two sisters. Students can compare this tender relationship with the hostility and competition usually found among the sisters and brothers of folklore—and real life as well. THE GOLD BUTTONS—a story brought to Israel by refugees from Eastern Europe after World War II—shows the traditional Jewish trait of transforming disaster into blessing. Although a young nation, Israel already possesses an uncommonly rich and varied folklore, for her people bring their tales from all parts of the world.

So much for prologue—now for the plays!

Bricriu's Feast

Characters

BRICRIU (bri kroo), *a blustery lord*
LADY BRICRIU, *his shrill wife*
FIRST HERALD
SECOND HERALD
CONALL   }
CONCHOBAR (kong'ko war) }   *three warriors*
CU CHULAINN (kōō kul'in) }
COOK
WORKERS, *three or more*
ENTERTAINERS
GIANT (*under his sack-like garment he carries a pole topped by three awesome heads, one on top of the other. His costume conceals all but the topmost head. Each time he is beheaded he pokes his pole higher so that the next head shows.*)

Scene 1:

> *Banquet hall of the great lord* BRICRIU. *Several* WORKERS *prepare for a great feast with much hammering and scurrying. Two* HERALDS *on ladders stand guard.* BRICRIU *and* LADY BRICRIU *bark out orders.*

BRICRIU: You—Hammer down that plank.
LADY B: You—Hang the tapestry.
BRICRIU: Bring out benches.
LADY B: Set out tin drinking cups.
BRICRIU: Not tin cups, wife. Crystal goblets.
LADY B: Tin cups, husband. Our goblets are shattered.

BRICRIU: Who shattered my goblets?

LADY B: You yourself. (To a WORKER) You—Pick up that cushion.

BRICRIU: I? When?

LADY B: At our last feast. You found the wine sour, so you hurled goblets at all the guests.

BRICRIU: Well, sour wine stings my tongue. (To a WORKER) You—Pound that peg.

LADY B: At another feast you said the music was too loud so you tossed rocks at all the musicians.

BRICRIU: Loud noise pains by ears. (To WORKER) Stop that pounding.

LADY B: Remember when the light bothered your eyes so you knocked down a candelabra and set fire to the banquet hall? Oh, that temper of yours. (To WORKER) Don't drop it!

BRICRIU: What about your temper? Always screeching—

LADY B (Yells at WORKER): Clumsy!

BRICRIU: That sound! (*He claps his hand over her mouth.*)

LADY B: Mmmmmmph. (*Thrashes her way out of his grasp*) Brute! (HERALDS *appear.*)

FIRST HERALD: Three warriors wend their way.

BRICRIU: Aha—lords Conall, Conchobar, and Cu Chulainn.

SECOND HERALD: Their stride is swift; their bright swords sparkle.

LADY B (*In a flurry of primping*): Almost here! My earrings—

BRICRIU: Workers, be gone. (WORKERS *exit*.) Shall we greet our guests, my dear?

LADY B (*Grandly*): With pleasure, my lord. (*They start to leave, arm in arm.* COOK *enters.*)

COOK: How many at table, my lord?

BRICRIU: Why—ah—my lovely wife (LADY B *simpers*) —myself—and lords Conall—and Conchobar—and Cu Chulainn—(*Silence.*)

LADY B: And that's all?

COOK: Just five at table, my lord? (BRICRIU *nods.* COOK *shrugs and leaves.*)

LADY B: Husband—this feast—all the hammering and rushing and roasting—for only five people?

BRICRIU: I invited others, but they all refused.

LADY B: Aha. That violent temper of yours frightened them all away.

BRICRIU: That screechy voice of yours. (*He claps hand over her mouth.*)

FIRST HERALD: Three noble warriors await at the gate.

SECOND HERALD: Strong arms rise in greeting; strong fists pound the door.

BRICRIU: Undo the latch. Bid them enter.

LADY B (*Loudly*): Ha. Ha, ha. When those three enter this empty hall, how they will laugh. Ha. Ha, ha. The table is full, but the seats are empty. Ha, ha, ha.

BRICRIU (*Seizing her*): No one laughs at the great lord Bricriu.

LADY B: Oh—Bricriu—my lord—my arm!

BRICRIU (*Shoving her aside, pulling down draperies,*

and bellowing): No one laughs at Bricriu. Workers—
(WORKERS *enter.*)—drape yourselves in these costly
cloths. (*They obey.*)

LADY B: What a clever idea! (*To* WORKERS) Straighten
those shoulders; comb your hair; poke your noses in
the air. (WORKERS *strut about in grand manner.*)

BRICRIU: Behold Bricriu's banquet hall—filled with fine
guests.

LADY B: Your temper is quick, husband—but so is your
brain.

BRICRIU (*Fondling her*): These gems dangling at your
lobes, my love, have a saucy rhythm that sets my
fingers dancing. (*He tickles her neck; she giggles
girlishly. Meanwhile, WORKERS cluster in corner to
confer and conspire.*)

LADY B (*Giddily*): My lord—not now.

FIRST WORKER: My lord—

BRICRIU (*Still playing with wife's earrings*): W¹.at?

FIRST WORKER: We have decided not to atteאd your
feast.

BRICRIU: What!

LADY B: You dare turn down my husband's hospitality!

FIRST WORKER: We appreciate his invitation but—

SECOND WORKER:—but we fear his temper.

BRICRIU (*Looking around for something to throw*):
Why, you—

FIRST WORKER: My lord, how can we swallow our food
knowing that at any moment you may hurl rocks or
goblets—(BRICRIU *seizes candelabra.*)

SECOND WORKER:—or set fire to the banquet hall.

BRICRIU (*Brandishing candelabra*): Ungrateful, ill-mannered, ignorant—

LADY B (*Screeching*): Husband! (BRICRIU *cringes at her cry.* LADY B *stretches out hand for candelabra.*)

LADY B (*Softly and sweetly*): Let me take that from you, my lord. Thank you, my lord. (*To* WORKERS) See—speak softly and he becomes gentle as a lamb.

THIRD WORKER: Perhaps we should stay—

SECOND WORKER: There is a whole boar roasting over the fire.

THIRD WORKER (*Sniffing*): That smell—it sets my tongue a-flutter. (*He flutters his tongue.*)

LADY B (*Sweetly*): Pray, stay—(*Sternly*) or my husband will get so angry he will take a deep breath causing each hair on his head to be drawn into his scalp and when he exhales—the force of his breath will knock you down senseless.

FIRST WORKER: We'll stay; we'll stay.

LADY B: How nice.

BRICRIU (*Offering* LADY B *his arm*): My lady. (*They exit with great dignity. The elegantly draped* WORKERS *strut after them as curtain falls.*)

Scene 2:

Same as Scene 1. BRICRIU, LADY BRICRIU, CONALL, CONCHOBAR, CU CHULAINN, *and* WORKERS *are seated at table, enjoying music and acrobatics performed by a troupe of* ENTERTAINERS. *A platter of cabbages and other harvest foods decorates table. There is also a great jug of mead or wine at hand.*

CONALL: Quiet. Silence. A toast to our host. (*All toast and cheer.*)

BRICRIU: And I toast the bravest warriors of our land—Conall, Conchobar, and Cu Chulainn. (*All cheer.*)

CONCHOBAR: And I toast our gracious hostess with precious gems dancing from her earlobes.

ALL: Aaaaaaah! (LADY B *simpers.*)

CU CHULAINN: I toast all these lords (*Indicating* WORKERS)—the best-dressed company I have ever toasted. (WARRIORS *applaud;* WORKERS *smirk and nudge each other.*)

BRICRIU: Friends—we've toasted one toast; now let's eat the roast.

LADY B: Cook—(COOK *enters carrying platter with roasted boar.* ENTERTAINERS *play musical fanfare.* HERALDS *appear.*)

FIRST HERALD: A huge creature approaches. (LADY B *gasps, clutches* BRICRIU.)

SECOND HERALD: A giant comes.

(WORKERS *and* ENTERTAINERS *flee.*)

FIRST HERALD: Broad of shoulder, fat of mouth—

SECOND HERALD: Bulging eyes and bristly face—

FIRST HERALD: Ugly, wrinkled, bushy-browed—

SECOND HERALD: Hideous and horrible—

FIRST HERALD: Strutting and striding—

SECOND HERALD: Sneering and snarling—(GIANT *lumbers on stage, brandishing club and snarling.*)

GIANT: I smell the smell of roasted boar.

BRICRIU: Cook—be gone! (COOK *starts to leave.*)

LADY B: Cook—come back! (*To* BRICRIU) Let the Giant take the meat.

BRICRIU: And let my guests go hungry? Never! (*To* COOK) Leave.

(GIANT *snarls.*)

LADY B (*To* COOK): Stay. (*To* BRICRIU) Better hungry than slain.

GIANT: Meat, meat.

BRICRIU: Monster—you want meat? Then fight for it! (COOK *exits.*)

LADY B: Dear husband—how fearless you are!

BRICRIU: Ah—well—it is not I, but these three brave warriors who will battle the giant.

GIANT: Fight, fight.

BRICRIU: Lord Conall, please tickle this fellow with your sword so we can dine without distraction.

CONALL: I came here to feast, not fight. (*He throws down sword and stalks off.*)

GIANT: Fight, fight.

BRICRIU: Lord Conchobar, before you taste boar, will you first savor swordplay?

CONCHOBAR: With no food in my belly, I have no appetite for combat. (*He drops sword, makes apologetic gesture, and leaves.*)

GIANT: Fight, fight.

LADY B (*To* BRICRIU): You and your brave warriors!

BRICRIU: Silence, screech owl, or I'll send *you* to defend

our meal. (*To* CU CHULAINN) Well, Lord Cu Chulainn—what is *your* excuse?

CU CHULAINN: Why, I have none. (*Snatches up the two swords dropped by his companions and confronts* GIANT) Ho, colossal clod, you are about to lose your head.

GIANT: Behead me—then I behead you.

BRICRIU (*To* LADY B): Great numbskull—thinks his head is like some garden posy—snip if off, and a prettier bloom will appear. (COOK *re-enters carrying boar.*)

COOK ⟨̶ ̶ ̶ ̶ ̶ ̶⟩

BRICRIU: ⟨̶ ̶ ̶ ̶ ̶⟩ s soon enough.

OOK (*To* CU CHULAINN): My lord—

CU CHULAINN: Stop trembling, man, and speak.

COOK: That is no ordinary giant—but a three-headed one! (*He flees.*)

CU CHULAINN: Why, then I must find me two more heads. Aha— (*Snatches two cabbages from the table and sticks them on his two swords*) There! We are evenly matched. (*He knocks off* GIANT'S *head.* GIANT *reels and groans, then produces second head.*)

LADY B (*Whispering to* BRICRIU): This new head is no handsomer than the first. (GIANT *clubs cabbagehead and sword out of* CU CHULAINN's *left hand.* CU CHULAINN *knocks off* GIANT's *second head.* GIANT *knocks second cabbage and sword out of* CU CHU-LAINN's *grasp.* CU CHULAINN *unsheathes his own*

sword and smites off GIANT's *third head.* GIANT
*now appears headless since his own head is concealed
under costume.*)

GIANT (*In shrill, shaky voice*): My heads, my heads. (*He
stumbles offstage.*)

CU CHULAINN: Wait, little Giant. Stay for the meat.

LADY B: How would he eat without any mouth? (*All
laugh.*)

BRICRIU: Heralds, announce the brave deeds of the war-
rior Cu Chulainn.

FIRST HERALD: Cu Chulainn, a good man he.

SECOND HERALD: Comely and quick—

FIRST HERALD: Swift and smart—

SECOND HERALD: Of strong will and skilled sword—

FIRST HERALD: Cut down the Giant—

SECOND HERALD: Smote him to small size—

FIRST HERALD: Drove off the cringing coward—

SECOND HERALD: Far from the fine feast.

BRICRIU: Workers, minstrels—danger's past. Re-enter
the hall! (*All except* CONALL *and* CONCHOBAR *return.*)

LADY B: Cook—the roast!

(Cook *enters with platter of boar.* ENTERTAINERS
*play musical fanfare and perform acrobatics. All dine
and celebrate.*)

Curtain

Till
Eulenspiegel's
Merry Pranks

Prank One: **THE GIFT HORSE**

Characters

TILL
MERCHANT

Setting:

In front of curtain. A tree is at one side. TILL enters, riding hobby horse Brunhilde. He trots back and forth, humming. He plucks blossom from tree and attaches it to horse's tail.

TILL: Ah, Brunhilde, my silken-haired beauty! (MER-CHANT, *laden with pots, enters. His burden clanks noisily.*)

MERCHANT: Out of my way, knave!

TILL: Good morning, friend.

MERCHANT: Bah! My feet hurt.

TILL: Well then, sit under this tree with me—

MERCHANT: No time to sit. Have to rush. Get to market. Sell pots. Make money, lots of money—

TILL: Too bad. We could have had a nice talk. (*He starts to mount horse.*)

MERCHANT: Wait. Sell me your horse.

TILL: My beloved Brunhilde? Never! (*He hugs horse, strokes mane, fluffs tail.*)

MERCHANT: Two gold pieces for that nag.

TILL: Nag! (*To horse*) Don't listen to him, dear heart.

MERCHANT: Three.

TILL: Absolutely not.

MERCHANT: Four.

TILL: Not four, not five, not ten.

MERCHANT: Eleven!

TILL: Listen, pot-seller, I tell you frankly—I don't like you. You're rude and crude and I don't want your money.

MERCHANT: Twelve?

TILL: Pot-seller, you really want my horse?

MERCHANT: Why do you think I'm bargaining, nincompoop?

TILL: Then take her as a gift.

MERCHANT: What! You're trying to trick me—

TILL: I dislike you so much that I'm willing to give you my horse free—if you let me hit you three times.

MERCHANT: Rogue! What do you take me for?

TILL: Why, for a shrewd businessman who knows a good bargain.

MERCHANT: Bargain. Hmmmmm—

TILL: A few instants of pain, and you'll have yourself a fine steed.

MERCHANT: Agreed.

TILL (*To horse*): Ah, Brunhilde, how I'll miss you. Those many happy—

MERCHANT (*Interrupting*): Don't dilly-dally. I'm a busy man. Have to make money, beautiful money, shiny gold—(TILL *gives him a hearty thwack.*) OW! Oh, my back—(TILL *strikes again.*) Oh! ow! (TILL *starts to ride away.*) Wait. Hit me again. You promised—

TILL: Friend, you need time to recover. I'll come back another day to give you the third blow.

MERCHANT: But the horse—you promised—

TILL: She's yours—(*Tossing his flower from horse's tail*) as soon as I deliver the third blow.

MERCHANT: Scoundrel! Horsethief!

TILL: Giddap, Brunhilde. (*He gallops off with MER-CHANT in hot pursuit, pots clattering. Curtain opens for Prank Two.*)

*　　*　　*

Prank Two: **LOST AND FOUND**

Characters

TILL
INNKEEPER

Setting:

> *Door marked "Inn" on one side of stage. TILL enters on foot and approaches door. He turns to call offstage to his horse.*

TILL: Rest in the stable, Brunhilde, while I get some dinner. (*Offstage neighing*) What? You'll miss me? Now, now—I won't be long—and I'll bring you a nice lump of sugar when I return. (*Sound of neighing. TILL knocks at Inn door.*)

INNKEEPER: (*Opens door.*) We don't want any. (*He slams door. TILL knocks again. He opens door.*) You again!

TILL: Wait. (*As INNKEEPER tries to close door.*) I'm not selling anything. I just want some dinner.

INNKEEPER: No room at the table. (*He tries again to close door.*)

TILL: Please—I'm hungry.

INNKEEPER: Come back later.

TILL: Very well. Meanwhile I'll go back to the stable and look for my money.

INNKEEPER: Money?

TILL: Yes. (*Pulling pocket inside out*) Several gold coins. I must have dropped them while I was tying my horse, but I was too hungry to search through the straw. I'll go back now and—

INNKEEPER: My dear friend, I cannot turn away a hungry traveler. Come in.

TILL: I'll come back later.

INNKEEPER: Nonsense. (*Pulling him in*) You'll starve.

TILL: You said there's no room.

INNKEEPER: Take *my* seat. Eat *my* dinner. I'm getting too fat anyway.

TILL: Oh, sir—

INNKEEPER: Eat, eat. I'll keep your horse company so she won't get lonely. (INNKEEPER *shoves* TILL *into Inn, and then scurries offstage to stable. No one is on stage now, but voices of* TILL *and* INNKEEPER *are heard.*)

TILL: Oh—roast beef, potatoes—

INNKEEPER (*Sound of neighing*): Aha, here's his horse—

TILL:—buttered beans and buttered buns—

INNKEEPER:—then the money must be nearby—

TILL:—a big bowl of fresh strawberries—

INNKEEPER:—up to my elbows in straw. Why haven't I found any coins?

TILL:—this cake—six inches high and light as a feather— (*Sound of neighing; then a loud blow is heard.*)

INNKEEPER: Ow! That nag of his kicked me in the seat—Oh, what pain! (*He runs onstage clasping his backside.*)

TILL (*Stepping out of Inn, patting his stomach*): Ah, what food!

INNKEEPER: Your horse kicks like a mule and I couldn't find your money.

TILL: Frisky Brunhilde. She'll calm down when I give her some sugar.

INNKEEPER: How can you talk of sugar when you've lost all your money?

TILL: Oh, money—why!—(*Jingling pocket*) Fancy that! The coins were in my other pocket all this time!

INNKEEPER: Scoundrel! You tricked me out of my dinner.

TILL (*Making speedy exit*): Friend, I was merely helping you go on a diet!

* * *

Prank Three: **THE CURE**

Characters

TILL
NURSE
PATIENTS, five *people pretending to be sick*

Setting

> *Same as for Prank Two.* NURSE *comes out of Inn. She flips "Inn" sign so that it now reads "Hospital." The* PATIENTS—*moaning and groaning*—*file onstage and into Hospital. As they shuffle through doorway, they describe their symptoms to* NURSE.

FIRST PATIENT: Ooooh, I have a splinter.

SECOND PATIENT: Ooooow, my pinky is stiff.

THIRD PATIENT: I sneezed three times this morning. Kerchoo—that makes four.

FOURTH PATIENT: Aaaaah, how my toenail aches.

FIFTH PATIENT: Ich, my teeth itch. (NURSE *sighs, shakes her head, spreads her hands in a gesture of exasperation. She follows* PATIENTS *into Hospital. Stage is empty. Then* TILL *enters on horseback.*)

TILL: We'll surely eat well today, Brunhilde. Now that it's harvest time the villagers will be using their home-grown corn for delicious corn bread, corn muffins, corn fritters, corn syrup—a-a-a-ah— (*He stops talking to admire* NURSE, *who has just emerged from Hospital carrying a sign.*) well, hello!

NURSE: Hello. (*She posts sign, which says "Standing Room Only."*)

TILL: Standing room only! At a hospital?

NURSE: Yes. All our beds are filled.

TILL: There must be a lot of sick people in this village.

NURSE: Huh! Not sick. Lazy. All those who don't want to work in the cornfields come to the hospital pretending to be sick. At harvest time our beds are always filled with liars.

TILL: Ah, a pretty girl like you shouldn't frown. Forget your troubles and come dancing with me.

NURSE: I'd love to—No! A nurse shouldn't desert her patients.

TILL: But they're not sick.

NURSE: Well—telling lies is a kind of sickness. I'd better stay here.

TILL: If you won't desert your patients, I'll make them desert you.

NURSE: You don't know these lazy villagers. There's no way to get them out of our beds.

TILL: Hmmm. If I think of a way, will you come dancing with me?

NURSE: With pleasure.

TILL (*Opens Hospital door and calls inside*): Ho—in there! You poor sick people—(*Sounds of moaning and groaning: "oh, ow, aaaah"*)—I am going to give you medicine—(*More groaning*)—which tastes very good (*Sounds of pleasure: "ah, aha, oooh, mmmm".*) It may not cure you—(*More groaning*)—but will positively make you feel better. (*Sounds of pleasure.*) (TILL takes *handful of sugar cubes from pouch on his belt.*)

TILL (*Whispering to Brunhilde*): Forgive me, Brunhilde, for giving away some of your delicious sugar cubes. (*To* NURSE) Here. Give each patient one of these. (NURSE *disappears into Hospital.* TILL *passes the time by strolling about, dancing, humming, grooming horse, sprucing up his own appearance. Then he goes to Hospital door and calls inside.*)

TILL: Ho there! How do you like that medicine? (*Sounds of pleasure*) Did it cure you? (*Moans and groans*) Too bad. But you do feel better, don't you? (*Sounds of pleasure*) Very good. (*Starts to walk away, then turns back*) Oh— I forgot to tell you—if a liar takes that medicine he will turn red as a ripe tomato. (*Moans and groans*) So look around. If you see any tomato-heads in those beds, chase them into the fields to harvest the crops or there won't even be a single cornflake to eat this winter. (*Loud groans and sounds of people hitting one another are heard: "Oh, ouch, hey!"*)

TILL (*To horse*): Now, Brunhilde, you'll see how the sickness of lying can be cured by sweet sugar and strong words. (*Red-faced* PATIENTS, *pushing and shoving one another, stumble out of Hospital. Each pokes the person in front of him and accuses the one behind.*)

FIRST PATIENT: Red-faced liar!

SECOND PATIENT: Tomato-head!

THIRD PATIENT: Lazy loafer!

FOURTH PATIENT: Get into the fields and work!

FIFTH PATIENT: Because of you the whole village almost starved. (PATIENTS *chase one another offstage.*)

TILL (*Calling into Hospital*): Well, Nurse—are all the beds empty?

NURSE (*From inside Hospital*): Every single one. (*She twirls out of Hospital wearing her dancing skirt.*)

TILL (*Dazzled by her loveliness*): Aha!

NURSE: Well, what are you waiting for? Aren't you going to take me dancing?

(TILL *seizes* NURSE *and they dance off.*)

Curtain

The
Seagull Trap

Characters

GIRL, *an Eskimo teenager in boots and parka*
MOTHER
PRINCE OF SEAGULLS, *in a feathered cloak*
GULLS, *six or more, all wearing feathered cloaks*

Scene 1:

> *On the ground in front of curtain are several seagull traps.*
> *GIRL strides on stage, swinging a string of fish. She sees*
> *empty traps.*

GIRL: Those thieving seagulls! Stole every bit of bait from my traps. Oh—(*Stamps, shakes fist*) oh, those thieves! (MOTHER *enters, holding needlework.*)

MOTHER: Daughter! You screech like a loon!

GIRL: I baited these traps with fresh pink salmon—and look, not even a fishbone remains.

MOTHER: Clever seagulls—they fill their bellies and fly away free. (*She starts to sew.*)

GIRL: You don't even care that I must return to the village empty–handed.

MOTHER: It is not fitting for a girl to be a hunter.

GIRL: Oh, all you want me to do is sit in the igloo and sew. (*Hands MOTHER string of fish*) Hold these, please, while I make the traps stronger.

MOTHER: To use a needle is a useful skill.

GIRL: Mother, anyone can sew.

MOTHER: Ah, but only a skilled seamstress knows how to stitch furs into a snug garment that keeps out snow and wind.

GIRL: I would rather know how to trap seagulls. (*Reaches out for fish*) The bait, please.

MOTHER (*Handing over fish*): Daughter, when a man seeks a wife, he wants a helpmate, not a hunter.

GIRL: So that's why you want me to learn sewing—to trap a husband!

MOTHER: Is it a bad thing for a mother to want her daughter to marry well? (*Noise from offstage is heard.*) What's that?

GIRL: A gull! Quick—hide! (*She pulls MOTHER offstage.*) (*PRINCE OF SEAGULLS enters, looks around, tries to snatch salmon from trap, but cannot. He pulls so hard that trap gets dragged along with fish.*)

GIRL (*Rushing onstage*): So now you try to steal my trap, you thief. Oh, no—oh, no, you don't (*She holds onto trap. Tug-of-war between GIRL and PRINCE.*) Thief, if you fly off with this trap you must take the trapper as well. (*PRINCE pulls harder; GIRL lurches forward.*) Oh, this gull has the strength of an eagle. Oh—oh—(*She clings to trap as PRINCE pulls her through curtain.*)

Scene 2:

Curtain rises on Kingdom of the Seagulls—a polar landscape with whiteness all around. Many GULLS in feathered cloaks whistle, caw, and flap when PRINCE drags GIRL before them.

SECOND GULL: See her fingers fly.

THIRD GULL: As though they had wings.

FOURTH GULL: Behold the power of that shining silver of metal.

GIRL (*Sulking in cage*): Such fuss over an ordinary sewing needle.

PRINCE: Listen, demon—the arrow of a hunter can only destroy, but the seamstress's needle has the power to repair.

FIRST GULL: Your Highness, my cloak needs mending, too.

SECOND GULL: And mine.

THIRD GULL: These three feathers need to be stitched in place.

FOURTH GULL: Make the elder demon do all our mending.

MOTHER: All right. All right. But let my daughter out so she can help.

PRINCE: Very well. (*He frees* GIRL.)

GIRL (*Whispering*): Mother, I've never sewn feathers before.

MOTHER: Watch. In and out, in and out. Now you try it. (GIRL *takes over stitching of* PRINCE's *cloak*.) Who's next? (FIRST GULL *comes forward to be mended. The other* GULLS *dance around* MOTHER, GIRL, PRINCE, *and* FIRST GULL.)

GULLS (*Singing or chanting as they dance*):
Needle in and needle out,
Make the stitches tight,
When the demons mend our wings,

We'll soar once more in flight!

GIRL (*Finished stitching*): There!

PRINCE (*Examining cloak*): Ah, perfect.

GIRL: Why—thank you.

MOTHER (*Finishes with* FIRST GULL): Who's next?

SECOND GULL: See this rip at the bottom. (MOTHER *stitches.*)

THIRD GULL (*To* GIRL): These feathers are about to fall off.

GIRL: My needle will hold them fast. (*She sews while* PRINCE *watches.*)

PRINCE: So—the hunter is transformed into a seamstress.

GIRL: It is not fitting for a girl to be a hunter.

PRINCE: I have often wished for a skilled needlewoman to help care for my people. Will you marry me, seamstress, and rule at my side?

GIRL: Yes—no—Oh, I don't know. (*She finishes sewing feathers for* THIRD GULL.)

THIRD GULL: Ah, now I can fly more gracefully. (*He flutters around; other* GULLS *follow, testing their mended cloaks.*)

PRINCE: You do not find me pleasing!

GIRL: I do, but—

MOTHER: Daughter, a chance to marry a Prince!

GIRL: But marriage is a trap. Stitching and mending all day long. Oh, no, I want to be free. Free as a bird! (*She points to fluttering* GULLS.) PRINCE *blows birdwhistle. More* GULLS *enter, bearing cloak of white feathers.*)

GIRL: How beautiful.

PRINCE: A cloak for a bride.

MOTHER: Daughter, try it on. (GULLS *attempt to put cloak on* GIRL, *but she darts away*.)

GIRL: No. You're all trying to trap me. Needle in and needle out, forever and ever. No, I refuse to marry.

PRINCE: Very well—but she who accepts the bride's cloak has the power to fly.

GIRL: To fly! Oh—

PRINCE: Marry me and you'll really be free.

GIRL: Free as a bird! Oh, yes! Quickly, the cloak. (GULLS *arrange cloak on her shoulders.*) How does it look? Mother, smile. Soon I'll be both married and free.

MOTHER: I suppose you'll fly off every day and leave all the mending of the kingdom for me.

FIRST GULL: Let the Gull people share your work.

SECOND GULL: Just teach us to use your needle.

THIRD GULL: Yes, let each do his own mending.

FOURTH GULL: Then we'll all be free to fly.

GULLS (*dancing as they sing*):
   Needle in and needle out,
   The demon's tool we'll ply,
   When each knows how to mend his cloak,
   We'll all be free to fly.

PRINCE: Mother-in-law, put down your sewing and join the wedding dance. (*All dance.*)

Curtain

The King
Meets
His Match

Characters

RIMA
SIMA } *three pretty jackals, wearing bracelets*
FATIMA } *of bells at wrists and ankles*
KING } *two lions*
PRINCE }

Setting:

At dusk, a clearing in the jungle. RIMA, SIMA, and FATIMA dance and frolic around the edge of a pond. Now and then they bend to drink the clear water. KING and PRINCE approach. They attempt to scare off the JACKALS.

KING: Grrrrrrrrr!

RIMA: Oh, be quiet.

SIMA: Scat.

KING: You try, son.

PRINCE: Ahem. Grrrr. (FATIMA *giggles.*) Grrrrrrrrr. (JACKALS, *not at all frightened, join paws and resume dancing. They purposely crowd* LIONS *away from pond.*)

KING: Why, you inconsiderate, disrespectful little— Grrrrrrrrr. (*Stamps and stomps, bares fangs, trying to chase* JACKALS *from pond*) Come on, son. Got to scare away these—Grrr—rambunctious—Grrrrr—impudent—Grrrrr—jackals.

PRINCE: Grrrr. Grrrrrrrrrr. (*He too stamps, stomps, and grimaces.* RIMA *and* SIMA *run to one side.*) Grrrrrrrrrrr. (FATIMA *darts around* PRINCE, *tweaks* his tail. *Evading his grasp, she scampers off to join her sisters.*) Grrrrr. What a bunch. (LIONS *drink and refresh themselves at pond. JACKALS huddle together, whispering, giggling, and gesticulating. The following dialogue is simultaneous.*)

PRINCE: Aah. Nothing like cool pond water.

KING: Those young Jackals just don't know their place.

PRINCE: Forget them and come for a dip. (PRINCE *romps in pond. KING wades and sprinkles himself in a dignified manner.*)

KING: At one time every creature in the jungle respected the lion's strength, courage, and ferocious roar. Grrrrrr. But nowadays—(JACKALS' *bells interrupt him.*)

PRINCE: What a racket.

KING: Grrrr. Grrrrrrrr. (JACKALS *sashay past* LIONS, *ignoring roars.*)

SIMA: Pardon us.

RIMA: Jackals get thirsty, too, you know.

FATIMA (*Tousling KING's mane as she passes*): Old Curlylocks thinks he owns the whole pond.

KING: Grrrrrrrr. (*Thrashes about in horrendous rage, accidentally kicks boulder.*) Ooooooooow. (JACKALS *cover their smiles with their paws. FATIMA giggles.*)

PRINCE: Don't you Jackals realize my father is King of the jungle?

RIMA: So what!

KING: Grrrrrrrrr.

SIMA: Temper, temper.

RIMA: Tiresome old King.

SIMA: Always spoiling our fun.

RIMA: If only we could scare him.

FATIMA: His son has the silkiest mane.

SIMA: Don't change the subject.

RIMA: Sisters—I just thought of how to frighten the king. Listen—(JACKALS *conspire, then strut back towards the pond, their bells a-jingle.*)

PRINCE: How dare you make fun of the strongest, bravest, most ferocious—

FATIMA: He is not.

PRINCE (*Seizing her arm*): Silence!

KING: I'll tear her apart. (*He reaches out, but* RIMA *and* SIMA *block his grasp.*)

RIMA: Relax, old boy.

SIMA: Our sister speaks the truth.

KING: Out of my way!

FATIMA: You are no longer the mightiest beast in the jungle—(PRINCE *tries to silence her.*) Make him let go and I'll tell you who has taken your place.

KING: Another being rules the jungle?

PRINCE: She lies.

KING: Let go. Let her speak.

PRINCE: Her words mean nothing, Father. Empty sounds.

KING: Let her go. (*Shoves* PRINCE *away from* FATIMA) Speak, Jackal.

FATIMA: Every night, Lion (*Lights dim*), by the light of the moon (*Lights dim further*), to this very pond comes —Bharavi—he who is strong as an elephant, brave as a bull, with a roar like heaven's thunder.

RIMA, SIMA, FATIMA (*Huddling together in exaggerated fright*): Bharavi! Ooooooooh!

PRINCE: Bharavi—Bah! An imaginary monster to frighten children with. (*Lights shines brightly.*)

RIMA: Sisters, the moon!

SIMA: Let us leave before the coming of—Bharavi.

FATIMA: Bharavi!

RIMA, SIMA, FATIMA: Oooooooh! (*They run offstage. Lights dim.*)

PRINCE: Father—

KING: Yes—?

PRINCE: Night falls quickly—

KING: Yes—

PRINCE: Perhaps we should leave—?

KING: Perhaps. No! Grrrrrr. This Bharavi—if he exists —cannot be mightier than I. Grrrrrrrr.

PRINCE: Father, you are still the strongest, bravest— (FATIMA *silently tiptoes onto darkened stage, breaks a twig, then runs off.*)

KING: What's that?

PRINCE: Just a dry twig falling.

KING: Silly jackals made me jumpy as a cat. (RIMA *tiptoes on stage, makes loud bellowing noise, vanishes.*) Bharavi!

PRINCE: Father, let's leave.

KING: Bharavi—he really exists.

PRINCE: Father, come.

KING: Yes, yes—No! Grrrrrrrrr. I'll stay and show him who is king. (RIMA, SIMA, FATIMA *stomp onto darkened stage, bellow in unison, run off.*)

PRINCE: Quick, behind this tree. (KING *and* PRINCE *hide. All is silent.*)

KING: This is ridiculous. (*Steps forward*) Grrrr! A king hides from no one. (*He strides through darkness.* RIMA *appears, snaps twig.* KING *twitches, but keeps striding.* SIMA *appears, bellows.* KING *jumps, but keeps striding.* RIMA, SIMA, *and* FATIMA *stomp and bellow in unison.* KING *leaps in fright, but calls out bravely.*) You call that a roar, Bharavi? Sounds more like a sneeze. (*Bumps into tree*) Out of my way, Bharavi.

PRINCE: That was the tree, Father.

KING: Oh. (*Backs off, bumping into another tree*) Aha, so here you are, Bharavi. (*Raises paws in boxing pose*) Defend yourself, monster.

PRINCE: Er—that's just another tree, Father.

KING: Too many trees. They block out the moon.

PRINCE: Look out! (KING *trips over branch, sprawls on ground.*)

KING: Grrr. That was no accident. That was a trap. Grrrrrr. Oh, to get my paws on that Bharavi!

PRINCE (*Tries to lead him through darkness*): Come to the pond, Father, where the moon is brighter.

KING: Let go, cub. I'll find my own way. (*He gropes towards pond. Light suddenly shines brightly.* KING *sees his own reflection in pond*) Bharavi! Oh, what a monster. Flee, my son. That ugly beast is no match for me. (*Pulls off his crown, throws it down*) Let him be king. Run. (*He runs offstage.*)

PRINCE: Father, come back. That was your own reflection. (RIMA, SIMA, FATIMA *prance onstage, giggling and jingling their bells. They bellow in fun to let* PRINCE *know they were pretending to be Bharavi.*)

PRINCE: I told him there was no Bharavi. (*Notices crown*) The crown! (*He picks it up, tries it on, admires his reflection in pond.*)

RIMA: Mmmmm. Very nice.

SIMA: Really suits you.

PRINCE: Thank you. (*Assumes a stern, kingly manner*) Mischief-makers. You shouldn't have teased the old king.

FATIMA: Then we'll tease the young one. (*She pulls his mane, tweaks his tail, and runs off. RIMA and SIMA, giggling and jingling, run after her. PRINCE runs after them, roaring mightily.*)

Curtain

Tiger's Wedding Day

Characters

TIGER, *a nervous bridegroom*
MONKEY, *a helpful pal*
PARROT, *a wing–flapping look–out*
ANANSI, *a mischievous spider*
BRIDE, *a lady tiger*
BRIDESMAIDS, *three or more jungle felines (leopards, panthers, or others)*

Setting:

> *In a lush green jungle,* TIGER *is dressing for his wedding.* MONKEY *helps.* PARROT *acts as look–out from his high perch—a vine–draped ladder.*

MONKEY: Well, Tiger—in another hour you'll be married.

PARROT: Are you nervous?

TIGER: Me? Not a bit. Where's my shirt? How can I get married without a shirt? Search! Leave no stone unturned.

PARROT: Tiger, look—!

TIGER: Where? Where?

MONKEY: Right in front of your nose.

TIGER: Oh. (*Tries to put shirt on*) Oh, no! It doesn't fit.

MONKEY: You've got it upside down.

TIGER: Oh.

PARROT: You're not a bit nervous, are you?

TIGER: Of course not. Oh, no, the buttons don't work.

MONKEY: You're just shaky. (*Buttons shirt*) Here, let me.

PARROT: Guests are arriving!

TIGER: So soon? Where's my tie? Who's here?

PARROT: Mr. and Mrs. Zebra. Miss Giraffe. The Baboon family.

TIGER: Oh, no! My tie won't tie.

MONKEY: I'll do it. (ANANSI *enters, wearing delivery-man's cap. He knocks at base of* PARROT's *ladder.* TIGER *hides.*)

ANANSI: Which way to the bridegroom's room?

TIGER: Go away. Nobody home. Pssst, Parrot—who's he?

PARROT: Just a delivery clerk.

ANANSI: Package from the florist.

TIGER (*Sticking head out of hiding place*): Must be for the bride.

MONKEY: The bride's bower is there—across the lake.

ANANSI: But this is a flower for the groom's lapel.

TIGER (*Coming forward*): I'm the groom.

ANANSI: Congratulations! (*He whips out trick flower and squirts water all over* TIGER's *shirt.*)

TIGER: Oh! Oh, no! I'm soaked. Have to find another shirt. (*He runs offstage.* ANANSI *pulls off cap, rolls around on ground, laughing heartily, waving his many legs.*)

MONKEY: Anansi the spider—always spoiling people's fun.

ANANSI: Serves him right. He didn't invite me to his wedding.

MONKEY: Who'd want to invite you anywhere? Always playing those nasty tricks.

ANANSI: Oh—some people just can't take a joke.

PARROT: That was no joke when you dipped my tail feathers in tar. (*To* MONKEY) Look, they're still stuck together.

MONKEY: He once sprinkled itching powder inside my pajamas. (*Scratches himself*) Wow, was that itchy! (TIGER *enters.*)

TIGER: I can't find a dry shirt. Cancel the wedding.

MONKEY: Here—just put your jacket on and no one will notice.

ANANSI: I'm telling. (*Shouts*) Listen everyone. Bridegroom has no shirt. Ha ha, ha ha. (*He rolls on floor, waving his legs.*)

TIGER (*Charging at* ANANSI): Spoilsport. Party-pooper. Blabbermouth.

ANANSI (*Scampering off*): Big striped pussycat—pick on someone your own size. (MONKEY *prevents* TIGER *from grabbing* ANANSI *as he leaves.*)

MONKEY: Relax. Don't spoil your own wedding day.

TIGER: If I could get my paws on him my wedding day would be perfect. (BRIDESMAIDS *enter.*)

FIRST BRIDESMAID (*To* TIGER): Aren't you ready?

SECOND BRIDESMAID: Everyone's waiting.

PARROT: Girls, you look like a bouquet of flowers.

MONKEY (*Inhaling*): They smell like flowers too. (*Sniffs* THIRD BRIDESMAID's *neck*) Aaaah.

THIRD BRIDESMAID: Oooooh, that tickles.

MONKEY: Will you save me the first dance?

THIRD BRIDESMAID: I was hoping you'd ask.

PARROT (*Singing*): Here comes the bride, all dressed in white—(BRIDE *enters*.)

BRIDE: Tiger—?

TIGER: Sweetie, you're so white and fluffy!

BRIDE (*Coyly primping*): Ooooh—

MONKEY: Like a big striped marshmallow.

BRIDE: Hmph. (*Sternly*) What's taking so long? People are restless. Don't dawdle. Move along.

TIGER: Yes, sweetie. Almost ready, sweetie.

BRIDE: Well, hurry. (*To* BRIDESMAIDS) Come along, girls. (*She bustles out with* BRIDESMAIDS *fluttering after.*)

PARROT (*Mimicking*): Yes, sweetie. Almost ready, sweetie.

TIGER: You making fun of me?

PARROT: Who, me?

MONKEY: Relax. He's a parrot. Parrots always repeat.

PARROT: Yes, sweetie. Almost ready, sweetie.

TIGER (*Starts to climb up after* PARROT): You quit that.

PARROT: Someone's coming. Someone's coming. (ANANSI, *in red–hooded cloak, carrying basket, comes skipping onstage, singing falsetto version of "Here Comes the Bride."*)

ANANSI: Here comes the bride, la la la la. I have a gift for the happy couple.

MONKEY: Please leave it at the bride's bower across the lake.

ANANSI (*In falsetto voice*): Oh, I've carried this heavy basket of goodies all the way from grandmother's house

(*Chattering faster and faster*) where-I-was-frightened-by-a-wolf-who-almost-gobbled-me-up-but-then-a-brave-hunter-came—

PARROT: Enough. Enough.

MONKEY: Bride's bower please, miss.

ANANSI: Oh, this basket is too heavy for little me to carry one more step—(*He collapses prettily.*)

TIGER: There, there, little lady. I'm the bridegroom—

ANANSI: You really are?

TIGER: Yes.

ANANSI: Then this is for you! (*Reaches into basket and tosses handful of white glop onto* TIGER) Ha, ha. Ha, ha.

TIGER: Hey, Stop. Don't. Oh, no! (MONKEY *grabs* ANANSI, *pulls off his red cloak.*)

MONKEY: Anansi! We should have known.

TIGER: I'll tear him to pieces.

ANANSI (*Scampering off*): Why so mad? Everyone throws rice at weddings.

MONKEY (*Throwing glop at* ANANSI *as he leaves*): But not rice pudding.

TIGER (*Pointing to globs of glop all over him*): Look at me!

MONKEY: Here, wear his cape. (*Drapes* ANANSI's *cape on* TIGER) Say, not bad.

PARROT: Here come the bridesmaids again. (BRIDESMAIDS, *clutching bouquets, enter weeping.*)

MONKEY: What's wrong, girls?

FIRST BRIDESMAID (*Sobbing*): Nothing.

SECOND BRIDESMAID (*Sobbing*): Nothing at all.

TIGER: Then why are you crying?

THIRD BRIDESMAID (*Sobbing*): We can't help it.

MONKEY (*Sniffing*): I smell something (*Sniffing*) that doesn't belong (*Sniffing* BRIDESMAIDS' *bouquets*) in a bouquet—(*Plucks onions out of bouquet*) aha!

BRIDESMAIDS: Onions!

TIGER: Another one of Anansi's tricks.

FIRST BRIDESMAID: Come on, girls. Let's pick fresh flowers. (BRIDESMAIDS *flutter out*.)

MONKEY: That mean spider. Trying to ruin the wedding just because he wasn't invited.

TIGER: Say—if he really wants to come, I'll invite him.

PARROT: Call off the wedding. The groom's gone crazy.

TIGER: Yessir, I'll invite him personally.

PARROT: Crazy, crazy.

TIGER: And I'll personally escort him—

MONKEY: Crazy, crazy.

TIGER:—right into the lake.

MONKEY: Oh-ho!

PARROT: Brilliant, brilliant. (*Sees someone coming*) Here he comes again—with water pistols.

MONKEY (*To* TIGER): Better take off that cape before he squirts it. (ANANSI *enters, disguised as a masked robber*.)

ANANSI: This is a stick-up.

TIGER: Please don't shoot. This is my wedding day.

ANANSI (*Shooting water pistol*): Serves you right for not inviting me. (*He pulls off mask and turns to run away*.)

TIGER: Anansi. Wait. Don't leave.

ANANSI: Aren't you mad?

TIGER: Of course not. I can take a joke.

ANANSI: But I got you all wet again.

TIGER: So what. The sun will dry me in no time.

MONKEY: Tiger's a good sport, isn't he, Anansi? (ANANSI *nods*.)

TIGER: And Anansi sure thinks up good tricks, doesn't he, fellows?

MONKEY (*Nodding*): Terrific sense of humor.

PARROT: Real comedian.

ANANSI: Why, thank you. I—I'm sorry I tried to spoil the wedding.

TIGER: Well, I'm sorry I didn't invite you. Anansi—

ANANSI: Yes?

TIGER: Would you—(MONKEY *winks at* PARROT) do me the honor—(PARROT *smothers a laugh*) of attending my wedding?

ANANSI: Well—

PARROT: Here come the bridesmaids. (BRIDESMAIDS *enter*.)

FIRST BRIDESMAID: Look, new flowers.

SECOND BRIDESMAID: No more onions.

THIRD BRIDESMAID: Smell!

MONKEY: Aaaaah.

TIGER: Girls, I've been trying to talk Anansi into coming to the wedding.

FIRST BRIDESMAID: What!

SECOND BRIDESMAID: Oh, no!

THIRD BRIDESMAID: Crazy, crazy! (PARROT *gestures them to be quiet*.)

ANANSI: See! No one wants me. I'm not going.

TIGER: Why, they're just joking—aren't you, girls? (BRIDESMAIDS *are mystified. They look at one another and shrug.*)

MONKEY: Tiger's going to escort Anansi personally—by way of the lake. (*Behind* ANANSI's *back* PARROT *holds his nose and pantomimes jumping into lake.*)

BRIDESMAIDS (*Enlightened at last*): Oh!

ANANSI (*Sulking*): Well, I'm not going.

TIGER: Anansi! (ANANSI *shakes his head.*)

MONKEY: Come on, girls. Coax him.

FIRST BRIDESMAID: Anansi, please come.

SECOND BRIDESMAID: Pretty please.

ANANSI: Coax me some more.

THIRD BRIDESMAID: The wedding won't be any fun without you.

SECOND BRIDESMAID: I'll dance the first dance with you.

ANANSI: How can I resist?

TIGER: Let's go. (BRIDE *enters.*)

BRIDE: What's taking so long?

TIGER: Good news, my love. Anansi's coming to our wedding.

BRIDE: If he comes, I won't.

TIGER: Sweetie, don't be that way.

BRIDE: He'll spoil everything.

TIGER: *You'll* spoil everything.

BRIDE: So that's the way you feel! (*Pulls off veil*) There! That's the end of our wedding. *She bursts into tears and runs off.* BRIDESMAIDS *follow.*)

TIGER (*To* ANANSI): It's all your fault.

MONKEY: As usual. (TIGER *and* MONKEY *push* ANANSI *towards lake*.)

ANANSI: No. Let go. I don't want to get wet.

PARROT: Here comes the bride. (BRIDESMAIDS *drag* BRIDE *onstage*.)

BRIDE: No. Let go. I don't want to get married. (TIGER *and* MONKEY *shove* ANANSI *into lake*.)

ANANSI: Glub!

BRIDE: Oh! (*She and* BRIDESMAIDS *giggle as they watch* ANANSI *splash and flounder*.)

TIGER: Sweetie, now can we go ahead with the wedding?

BRIDE: I was hoping you'd ask. (MONKEY *dusts off veil and hands it to* BRIDE.)

PARROT (*Singing*): Here comes the bride. . . . (*All sing and march off.* ANANSI *crawls out of lake and trails after them, gulping along in tune*.)

ANANSI: Glub-glub glub-glub.

Curtain

Alenka
and
Aliona

Characters

ALENKA, *a lovely young woman*
ALIONA, *her younger sister, who becomes the* FAWN
HAG
KING
PAGE
SOLDIERS

Scene 1:

> *At daybreak,* ALENKA *and* ALIONA *are asleep in the woods.* ALENKA *stirs, stands, stretches, smiles at the sun.* ALIONA, *still asleep, pulls a tattered blanket around herself.*

ALENKA: Wake up, sister.

ALIONA: I'm thirsty.

ALENKA: Oh, Aliona—on a day this beautiful we'll surely find water and food and even someone to take care of us.

ALIONA: No one wants to care for two homeless orphans. (HAG *enters, her face almost hidden by a babushka. She carries a basket from which protrudes a long loaf of bread.*)

ALENKA: Good morning.

HAG: Hmph.

ALENKA: Beautiful day, isn't it?

HAG: Can't take a walk without being bothered.

ALENKA: What a long bread!

HAG: It's mine.

ALENKA: My sister and I—we're so hungry—

HAG: Here, here— (*thrusting bread at* ALENKA) just stop bothering me.

ALENKA: Oh, thank you. (HAG *hobbles offstage, cackling.*) Aliona—breakfast! (*Breaks bread in half*) Oh, it's all moldy inside.

ALIONA: What did you expect from that witch?

ALENKA: Why do you think she's a witch?

ALIONA: The way she laughed. (*She tosses her share of bread offstage; a splash is heard.*)

ALENKA: Aliona—that splash! (ALENKA *tosses her half in same direction; another splash is heard.* ALIONA *runs offstage.*)

ALIONA (*Calling from woods offstage*): A pond! I'm so thirsty.

ALENKA: Wait, sister. Don't drink!

ALIONA (*Still in woods offstage*): The water tastes strange. Alenka, I feel strange. Alenka—(ALIONA *emerges from woods as* FAWN. *She wears mask and leotard. Around her neck is a ribbon which she was wearing before her transformation.*)

ALENKA: A fawn—Aliona's ribbon—oh—oh, my dear sister! (*Sound of* HAG *cackling is heard.*) That witch—how can we undo her terrible spell? (KING *enters, carrying bow.* PAGE *follows, carrying arrows.*)

KING (*Seeing* FAWN): Quickly, boy. An arrow.

ALENKA: Oh no—don't shoot—(FAWN *flees.*)

KING: Gone! (*To* PAGE, *pointing at* ALENKA) Seize her!

ALENKA: No! Let go.

PAGE: You spoiled the King's hunt.

ALENKA: The King!

KING: On your knees, young woman, and perhaps I will pardon you.

ALENKA: No.

KING: You dare defy your sovereign!

ALENKA: I do not kneel to anyone who shoots at innocent animals.

PAGE: You'll pay dearly for that outburst.

KING: Young woman—

ALENKA: Yes, Your Highness?

KING: What is your name?

ALENKA: Alenka, Your Highness.

KING: Alenka—you are willing to defend your beliefs no matter how severe the punishment?

ALENKA: Yes, Your Highness.

KING: Hmmm. For many months I have sought a young woman of courage to help me rule. Alenka—will you be my Queen?

ALENKA: Oh—oh, Your Majesty—oh, yes! (FAWN *enters.*)

PAGE: Your majesty, the Fawn! (*He hands arrow to* KING.)

KING (*Rejecting arrow; then taking* ALENKA's *hand*): Never again will I shoot at innocent creatures of the forest. (KING *and* ALENKA *walk off hand in hand.* PAGE *follows.* FAWN *watches. Then* PAGE *turns, smiles at* FAWN, *and beckons her to follow. All exit as curtain falls.*)

Curtain

Scene 2:

Same as Scene 1, a month later. KING, *dressed for battle and flanked by uniformed* SOLDIERS, *bids goodbye to Queen* ALENKA.

KING: Turn back, dear wife. The woods are dangerous in time of battle.

ALENKA: How long will you be gone, husband?

KING: As long as it takes to win the war.

ALENKA: Take care, my dear—and hurry home. (KING *blows her a kiss, turns, and strides off.* SOLDIERS *follow.* ALENKA *stands forlorn. She sighs, wipes a tear from her eye.* PAGE *enters, leading* FAWN.)

PAGE: I brought the Fawn, Your Majesty, to ease your loneliness.

ALENKA: Thank you. And please tell the servants to prepare for the journey back to the palace.

PAGE: Yes, Your Majesty. (*He exits.*)

ALENKA (*To* FAWN): Aliona, the King is a good husband—but I won't be happy until you're restored to your true self. (HAG, *in cook's garb, enters, bearing tray of food.*)

HAG: A bit of nourishment before the journey home, Your Majesty?

ALENKA: Oh, I don't want to eat.

HAG: you must.

ALENKA: Why—don't tell me what I must do! Who are you anyway?

HAG: I? (FAWN *tries to butt at* HAG.) Be gone, animal.

ALENKA: She won't hurt you. (*To* FAWN) Aliona, behave. (*To* HAG) Now tell me who you are.

HAG: Why—I'm the new pastry cook. The King hired me to bake these special teacakes just for you.

ALENKA: In that case, I'll try one. (FAWN *tries to keep her from eating cake.*) Aliona, you almost made me drop it. (FAWN *butts* HAG *offstage.*) Aliona, you frightened her away. You're so strange today. This cake tastes strange—Everything's strange—(*She faints. FAWN circles around her frantically. HAG's cackle is heard offstage. FAWN runs away. All is still. HAG enters, cackling. She removes crown and robe from ALENKA's still form and puts them on herself.*)

HAG: Now the kingdom will meet a real queen. (*Struts in her royal garb and practices giving commands to imaginary people*) Servant, comb my hair; fasten my necklace. You—carve me a marble statue. Carpenters, build me a ship. (*Cackles gleefully, then addresses* ALENKA) As for you—into the magic pond. (*She drags* ALENKA *offstage. Splash is heard.* FAWN *enters, frantically searching for* ALENKA.)

ALENKA (*Singing offstage*):
Sister, dear sister, I lie in the magic pond,
Between my fingers water grasses grow,
Over my body sands shift and weeds float,
When my husband returns, the truth you will know.
(FAWN *sadly exits as curtain falls.*)

Curtain

Scene 3:

Same as Scene 1. KING and SOLDIERS enter from one side; PAGE enters from the other.

KING: Ah, my faithful page.

PAGE: Your Majesty!

KING (*To* SOLDIERS): See that the horses are fed. SOLDIERS *exit*.)

PAGE: Sire, I rejoice to find you both safe and victorious.

KING: Thank you—but why is my wife not here to greet me?

PAGE: The Queen—why—er—she was busy in the palace.

KING: Too busy to welcome her battle-weary husband?

PAGE: Oh, sire—prepare yourself. Your bride is utterly transformed.

KING: What? How so?

PAGE: Sire, she screams orders at the servants, spends all the money in the treasury, and forces the peasants to work until they collapse.

KING: Impossible! Not my gentle, generous Alenka. (FAWN *enters, circles* KING *in frantic manner*.) Well, Fawn, at least you haven't changed. (FAWN *shies away*.) Easy—be calm—you know I won't harm you.

PAGE: It's not you she fears, sire, but her own mistress.

KING: Then has Alenka changed so much that she frightens the very being whose life she once saved?

PAGE: The Queen has proclaimed that she herself will shoot the Fawn.

KING (*Seizing* PAGE): You're lying! All your words are false. It's you who will be shot for deceiving your sovereign.

PAGE: I swear, Your Majesty—all I report is the truth.

KING: Knave—I refuse to believe your monstrous tales. (FAWN *tries to help* PAGE.) Stand back, little Fawn. This troublemaker must be punished.

PAGE: If the Fawn could speak, she'd echo my truth. (*Unseen by* KING, HAG *enters. She wears* ALENKA's *robes and carries bow and arrow. She takes aim.*) Look!

KING (*Turning just in time to see HAG flee*): Alenka? No— (*To* PAGE) Your false tales have put false visions before my eyes.

ALENKA (*Singing offstage*):
Husband, dear husband, I lie in the magic pond
Between my fingers water grasses grow
Over my body sands shift and weeds float
Come seek me now and the truth you will know.

KING: Did the strain of battle put that strange song in my ear? I cannot distinguish between real and imaginary, false and true.

PAGE: That song was real; those words are true. Come! (*He runs offstage towards pond.* KING *hesitates, perplexed and despondent.* FAWN *gently prods him. He reaches out to her.*)

KING: Lead me, Fawn, for I know not where to go. (FAWN *leads him offstage. He cries out*) Alenka! Page —help me—(*Sound of splashing is heard.*) Gently, gently—ah, at last! (KING *and* PAGE *re-enter, supporting a drenched and unconscious* ALENKA, FAWN *follows.*) Page, faithful friend—forgive my harsh words.

PAGE: My only thought is for the Queen's safety.

KING: Watch over her, then—while I search for that evil imposter. (KING *exits.* FAWN *and* PAGE *care for* ALENKA.)

ALENKA (*Weakly moaning*): Ooooooh.

PAGE: You're safe, my Queen. (HAG, *disguised as a hunter, enters with bow and arrow.*) You—put down that weapon.

HAG: The King has commanded me to shoot the Fawn so that she will be released from her spell and become the Queen's sister.

PAGE: Her sister!

HAG: Yes—bewitched by a very powerful sorceress.

PAGE: Shoot, then, hunter. Let us have an end to this witchcraft. (HAG *aims at* FAWN. KING *enters.*)

KING: Don't shoot!

PAGE: Sire, you yourself gave the order.

KING: Not so! Who is this hunter? (HAG *cackles, pulls off hunter's disguise, and runs offstage.* KING *and* FAWN *pursue her.* HAG *screeches. A great splash is heard.*)

HAG (offstage): Aaaaaaagh.

ALENKA (Greatly revived): Husband—(KING enters.)

KING: Alenka—I'm here.

ALENKA: The witch—

KING: Gone forever. (ALIONA *enters.*)

ALIONA: Alenka—the spell is broken.

ALENKA: Sister—at last. (*The sisters embrace.*)

KING: Come, my dears. Let us return to the palace to celebrate. (*He takes* ALENKA's *arm.*) Page, please escort the Queen's sister. (KING *and* ALENKA *exit.*)

PAGE: With pleasure, Your Majesty. (PAGE *and* ALIONA *smile shyly at each other, then join hands. Music starts and the two exuberantly dance off.*)

Curtain

The
Gold
Buttons

Characters

ITZIG, *a villager*
RAYZEL, *his wife*
SHMERL, *a villager*
CHAVA, *his wife*
MAYOR
YACOB, *an old soldier*
YACOB'S SHADOW, *a puppet or mime*
YENTA, *wife of YACOB*
YENTA'S SHADOW, *a puppet or mime*
VILLAGERS, *several husbands and wives*

Shadows (Optional)

YACOB'S SHADOW—a live actor or cut-out puppet
YENTA'S SHADOW—a live actress or cut-out puppet

Setting:

A simple room with two rows of chairs

Production Note: This script includes stage directions for an optional Shadow Play within the main play. If you decide to stage it, include a sheet or screen in your setting and arrange a light so that SHADOWS will be seen when indicated in script. SHADOWS can be either live actors or simple cardboard puppets manipulated behind sheet by stage crew. The moving silhouettes will provide a lively and unusual background to accompany YACOB'S tale of woe.

For simpler staging, just ignore directions for Shadow Play and have YACOB and YENTA pantomime their own words as they speak.

VILLAGERS *enter couple by couple.* ITZIG *and* RAYZEL *greet* SHMERL *and* CHAVA.

ITZIG: Greetings, neighbors.

RAYZEL: What a flood that was!

CHAVA: Thank heavens the sun has finally dried our homes and fields.

SHMERL: So what good are dry fields when our crops are ruined?

RAYZEL: The Mayor! (VILLAGERS *hurriedly seat themselves,* MEN *in one row,* WOMEN *in the other. They applaud as* MAYOR *enters.*)

MAYOR: Fellow-citizens, what joy to be back in our village after those long weeks of flooding. (RAYZEL *raises her hand.*) Yes, citizeness?

RAYZEL: Is it permitted to sew?

MAYOR: Of course. (WOMEN *take out their sewing and knitting.*) Now that the disaster is over, do what you always do. Ladies cook and sew; men cultivate the fields.

SHMERL: So what is there to cultivate?

ITZIG: Your Honor, the flood washed away all our grain.

CHAVA: Nothing is left growing but dandelions.

RAYZEL: Yellow dandelions.

ITZIG: Acres of yellow dandelions.

MAYOR: A serious problem indeed. (*He strokes his beard.* MEN *stroke their beards.*) But surely all of us together can solve it. (MEN *shrug their shoulders.* WOMEN, *while stitching, shrug also.*)

ITZIG: The only solution is to ask neighboring villages for grain. (*All nod.*)

MAYOR: No! We are independent citizens, not beggars.

SHMERL: So if we don't beg, we starve.

CHAVA (*Shaking her head*): Can't bake bread from dandelions. (*All shake heads.*)

MAYOR: Dandelions—acres of yellow dandelions. (*A smile spreads over his face. He hums and does a little dance step.* VILLAGERS *are shocked.* WOMEN, *still stitching, shake their heads;* MEN *tap their heads to indicate that* MAYOR *is crazy.*)

SHMERL: Your honor—our crops are destroyed, our families are hungry—is this a time for singing and dancing?

MAYOR: Is it—or isn't it? Before we decide, let us listen to a story. (*Calling out*) Reb Yacob—(MEN *again tap their heads to indicate* MAYOR's *insanity.* YACOB *enters.*) Yacob, please tell us your adventures.

SHMERL: Is this a time for tale-telling?

MAYOR: Patience, patience. Proceed, Reb Yacob.

YACOB (*Sighs*): For thirty years I was a soldier. Then I retired. My wife and I moved to a little cottage where we raised chickens. (YENTA *bustles on stage.*)

YENTA: So tell them how many.

YACOB (*Introducing her to* VILLAGERS): My wife.

YENTA: We had five roosters and fourteen hens, so that yielded three dozen eggs at two pennies an egg—

YACOB: Enough, enough (*To* VILLAGERS): We were not rich—but we were not poor.

YENTA: We had three quilts, a rug for the floor, cake with raisins every Sabbath—

YACOB: Our life was pleasant and peaceful—

YENTA: Except when the grandchildren visited—Ah, such a racket! (WOMEN *nod in sympathy and murmur to one another.*)

RAYZEL: Little scamps.

CHAVA: They get on one's nerves.

RAYZEL: Crumbs all over the floor.

YENTA (*Fingering* RAYZEL's *embroidery*): Mmmm. Such nice, even stitches.

SHMERL: Is this a time for women's prattling?

MAYOR: Patience, patience. Continue, Reb Yacob.

YACOB: Very well. We lived on the profit from our eggs for many years. Then, one night—(*Stage darkens*) we heard a great clucking and squawking (*Sounds of clucking and squawking*) We ran to the chicken house. (Screen lights up. SHADOWS *of* YACOB *and* YENTA *appear behind it. They pantomime* YACOB's *narrative as he speaks*) All our chickens were gone. We ran back to the cottage—peered through the window—

YENTA: Thieves!

YACOB: They're taking everything we own—

YENTA: Our clothing, our furniture—(*Silhouettes of these articles pass behind Screen. The shapes are produced by cardboard cut-outs held up by unseen persons.*)

YACOB: The rug off the floor—

YENTA: The food from the cupboard—

YACOB: Even my old uniform—

YENTA: With buttons of gold—real gold. (*She bursts into tears.* WOMEN *weep in sympathy.*)

MAYOR: Ladies, ladies. Continue, Reb Yacob.

YACOB: After the thieves ran off, we tiptoed into our cottage. Nothing was left—

YENTA: Not even an egg.

YACOB: My wife wanted to ask the neighbors for help. (*Forgetting their audience of* VILLAGERS, YACOB *and* YENTA *argue with each other.* SHADOWS *echo their argument in mime.*)

YENTA: Just ask for a crust of bread, a blanket to cover us.

YACOB: No! Am I a man or a beggar?

YENTA: Is it so terrible to ask neighbors for help?

YACOB (*Shouting*): I don't lean on others when I can stand on my own two feet.

SHMERL (*Out-shouting* YACOB): Is this a time for domestic arguments?

MAYOR: Yacob, please—the rest of the story.

YACOB: Ah—yes—well, I decided to travel to the city to find work. (SHADOWS *bid each other goodbye.*) My wife stayed behind to guard the cottage. (*Sighs*) Yenta, I'm tired. You tell.

YENTA: I'll tell, I'll tell. (YENTA'S SHADOW *appears on Screen.*) For many weeks I lived alone. To keep busy I made a straw broom and every morning I swept the bare floor of our empty cottage. Then I wandered through the woods gathering nuts and berries for my meals. (*Screen shows woodland silhouettes produced by cardboard cut-outs. For example: a tree, a branch with berries, a bird flying, a rabbit scampering.*) Meanwhile, my husband was unable to find work in the city. Tired, hungry, and discouraged, he started the journey home. (*Screen shows bleak woodland images. For example: trees blowing in wind, bare branches, a wolf baying at moon,* YACOB'S SHADOW *trudging across Screen.*) The days were cold. All night the wind blew.

YACOB: How I suffered.

YENTA: You think I didn't suffer?

YACOB: You? You were snug in the cottage.

YENTA: Snug? Without firewood, without tea—not even a shawl to warm my shoulders.

YACOB: At least you had a roof over your head—

MAYOR: Yacob—get on with the story.

YACOB: She likes to talk. Let her tell.

YENTA: With pleasure. One morning (YENTA'S SHADOW *appears on Screen*), searching the woods for the last nuts of autumn, I saw something glitter. I stooped. Where is it? I poke through the fallen leaves. Aha—a gold button! Another! And another! Four buttons of real gold! What a harvest!

RAYZEL: From Yacob's uniform.

CHAVA: They fell off when the thieves escaped.

YENTA: So, dear ladies, who's telling this story?

YACOB: So don't listen to them.

YENTA: I should make myself deaf?

MAYOR: Yenta—the gold buttons.

YENTA: Ah, those beautiful buttons. I polished them on my sleeve until they shone like the sun. Then I rushed to the goldsmith and sold them for enough money to buy food and firewood—even a candle to brighten my dear husband's return. (YENTA'S SHADOW *lights candle, then leaves; Screen shows candle burning.*

Stage brightens and Screen goes blank. YENTA *goes to* YACOB) Yacob, I truly missed you.

YACOB: Without you, dear wife, I was truly lost.

RAYZEL (*Sighs sentimentally*): Aaaah.

CHAVA: Such a lovely story.

SHMERL: Our crops are ruined, our families hungry— is this a time for happy endings?

YENTA: So who said it's the end.

ITZIG: Then finish the story.

YACOB: She? She never finishes talking.

YENTA: I'm finished right now.

ITZIG: But what else happened?

MAYOR: Yacob—don't leave us in suspense.

YACOB: All right, all right. (*Stage darkens;* YACOB'S SHADOW *appears on Screen.*) Cold and footsore, whipped by the wind, I finally made my way home. Imagine my feeling when I saw that cheeful candle in the window—and a fine meal on the table.

RAYZEL: You were delighted.

YENTA: He was furious. He shook his fist, stamped his feet, shouting (*Imitating* YACOB's *voice*) "Beggar! I told you not to beg food and firewood from the neighbors!" (*In her own voice*) "Yacob, you're hurting me!" I cried, and quickly told him about the gold buttons. He was overjoyed. A warm smile came to his lips.

YACOB: I took your hands and asked your forgiveness.

YENTA: I forgave you.

YACOB: Then I seized your waist and we started to dance. (SHADOWS *dance off Screen, thus bringing*